BRAM STOKER'S

DRACULA

RETOLD BY MICHAEL BURGAN

Illustrated by José Alfonso Ocampo Ruiz
cover colour by Benny Fuentes
interior colour by Protobunker Studio

LIBRARIAN REVIEWER
Julie Potvin Kirchner
Educator

READING CONSULTANT
Elizabeth Stedem
Educator/Consultant

www.raintreepublishers.co.uk
Visit our website to find out
more information about
Raintree books.

To order:
☎ Phone +44 (0) 1865 888066
▤ Fax +44 (0) 1865 314091
▣ Visit www.raintreepublishers.co.uk

Raintree is an imprint of Capstone Global Library Limited, a company incorporated in
England and Wales having its registered office at 7 Pilgrim Street, London, EC4V 6LB –
Registered company number: 6695582

"Raintree" is a registered trademark of Pearson Education Limited, under licence to
Capstone Global Library Limited

Text © Stone Arch Books, 2009
First published by Stone Arch Books in 2008
First published in hardback in the United Kingdom in 2009
First published in paperback in the United Kingdom in 2010
The moral rights of the proprietor have been asserted.

Art Director: Heather Kindseth
Graphic Designer: Kay Fraser
Edited in the UK by Laura Knowles
Printed and bound in China by Leo Paper Products Ltd

ISBN 978-1406212549 (hardback)
13 12 11 10 09
10 9 8 7 6 5 4 3 2 1

ISBN 978-1406213560 (paperback)
14 13 12 11 10
10 9 8 7 6 5 4 3 2 1

British Library Cataloguing in Publication Data
Burgan, Michael.
Dracula. -- (Graphic revolve)
741.5-dc22
A full catalogue record for this book is available from the British Library.

TABLE OF CONTENTS

INTRODUCING . . .

Count Dracula

Jonathan Harker

Arthur Holmwood

Jack Seward

TABLE OF CONTENTS

INTRODUCING . . .

Count Dracula

Jonathan Harker

Arthur Holmwood

Jack Seward

4

Lucy Westenra

Mina Murray

Dr Van Helsing

5

CHAPTER 1: THE CASTLE OF HORROR

Deep in the heart of Transylvania, in the middle of Europe . . .

. . . a carriage raced through the wild night.

One of the passengers was Jonathan Harker, a lawyer from London.

What brings you to our country, Mr. Harker?
My company has sent me to meet with a local man. He wishes to move to England and needs help finding a home.
Perhaps you know him? His name is Count Dracula.
Dracula?!
Lord save us!

The count will never let me leave this place.

He plans to go to London without me.

The next morning, Jonathan returned to the room of coffins.

No, I will not let it happen.

The count now looked much younger!

I won't let him get to London.

17

Back in England, Mina Murray, Jonathan's girlfriend, waited patiently for him to return. That summer, she visited her old friend, Lucy Westenra.

Oh, Mina, it's so good to see you again.

Thank you for inviting me here to Whitby.

I needed to get away from the city.

It's hard being in London with Jonathan so far away.

He almost never writes, and I worry about him.

Enough about my troubles. How are you, Lucy?

The next day, Dr Van Helsing returned to check on Lucy. Jack had watched her through the night.

You'll never believe it. Lucy's neck is fine!

What?!

Does this mean she's better?

I'm afraid not, Jack.

It means we can do nothing for her now.

Meanwhile in London . . .

Jonathan, I'm so glad you've come home. I can't wait to tell Lucy!

Yes, and soon we'll —

I don't believe it!

What is it, dear?

Van Helsing had read Lucy's diary and learned about the strange beast in the garden.

The doctor is coming here tomorrow.

He thinks I might be able to help him understand what happened to Lucy.

And Jonathan? I think I should read your journal tonight.

The next day, Van Helsing arrived.

I know you're here about Lucy, but I must ask you something about Jonathan, too.

He has not been well!

This is his journal. Please read it, Doctor.

Strange marks on their necks.

Just like the ones we saw on Lucy.

Do you think the same creature that attacked Lucy bit these others?

It's much worse than that, Jack.

Lucy made these marks herself.

Lucy has become a vampire!

Dr Van Helsing, that is impossible!

There are creatures who are not alive, and yet not dead.

They are known as the undead, such as vampires.

There is an undead creature here in England, and Lucy was his first victim.

Now she is a vampire and needs blood. It is like food and water to her.

What can we do?

Van Helsing led Jack to the cemetery where Lucy Westenra was buried.

41

WHACK!

Now, we must seal the tomb with lead, and we are done . . . for now.

As Jack finished reading, the others arrived with Jonathan.

Mina showed me your journal, Jonathan. What an awful experience!

I hear you've had your own horrible time with Lucy.

Yes, one friend gone, and another almost dead, all because of Count Dracula.

He must be stopped!

What have you learned about him, Doctor?

He can command wolves, rats, and bats. If he wishes, he can also take the shape of these animals.

He has at least one home here in London.

I know where his new home is. It's not far from here, Doctor.
We must find the 50 boxes he shipped from Transylvania.
He can only rest in soil from his native land. Come along, gentlemen!
They soon arrived at Dracula's nearby house.
My friends, we face a terrible danger.
Before we enter this house, I have some items that will protect us.
A bottle of holy water.
A crucifix, like the one that saved Jonathan.
And a few sacred wafers. Keep them all close.

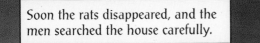

Soon the rats disappeared, and the men searched the house carefully.

How many boxes did you find?

Fewer than fifty. He must have sent the rest to other houses.

We must contact the shipping company and track them down!

49

51

Back at Jack's house, the men explained what happened to Mina.
But we must find him. We must kill him!
We? Mina, you're so weak now. What could you do?
Dracula said that he can control me. Our minds are linked.
If Dr Van Helsing can hypnotize me, I may be able to learn from Dracula's thoughts.
Is this possible, Doctor?

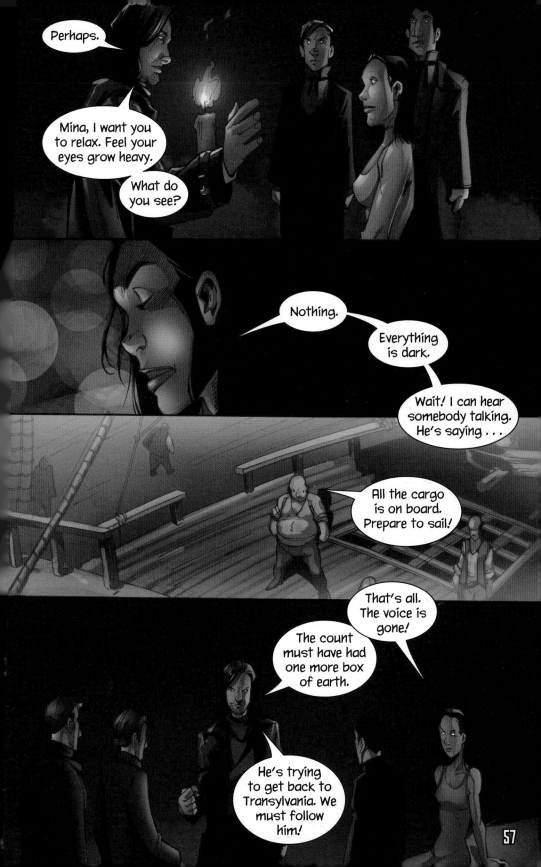

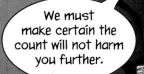

When they neared Transylvania, the vampire hunters learned that men had been hired to take Dracula's coffin into the mountains.

We should split up.

You three, follow the boat. Mina and I will try to reach the count's castle before he gets there.

Hours later, Dr Van Helsing and Mina could no longer see the road ahead of them. They were forced to pull over and camp for the night.

After they had lit their campfire . . .

Doctor! Who are they?

Do not fear, Mina. The holy wafers will keep these creatures from reaching us.

Jonathan and the others followed Dracula's wagon as it neared the castle.

Halt!

Unload the coffin, so we can search it.

Suddenly, Dracula rose from the fallen coffin.

Arrgghh!

Jonathan and the others followed Dracula's wagon as it neared the castle.

Halt!

Unload the coffin, so we can search it.

Suddenly, Dracula rose from the fallen coffin.

Arrgghh!

ABOUT THE AUTHOR

Bram Stoker was born on 8 November, 1847, near Dublin, Ireland. Young Stoker suffered from a mysterious illness. Until age seven, he spent much of his time in bed, reading books and dreaming of becoming a famous writer. After graduating from college, Stoker worked as a civil servant in Dublin Castle but continued to write stories in his spare time. He had also been interested in vampires and spent several years researching these legends. In 1897, *Dracula* was published. It remains his most famous story, inspiring countless movies, books, TV shows, and Halloween masks.

ABOUT THE RETELLING AUTHOR

Michael Burgan has written more than 90 fiction and non-fiction books for children. A history graduate from the University of Connecticut, USA Burgan worked at *Weekly Reader* for six years before beginning his freelance career. He has received an award from the Educational Press Association of America and has won several playwriting contests. He lives in Chicago with his wife, Samantha.

GLOSSARY

carriage (KA-rij) – a small vehicle with wheels, often pulled by horses

crucifix (KRU-sih-fiks) – a cross, which Christians believe represents Jesus Christ

curious (KYUR-ee-uhss) – a strong desire to investigate

journal (JUR-nuhl) – a book or notebook where someone records the daily events of his or her life, such as a diary

sacred wafer (SAY-krid WAY-fur) – a round, thin piece of bread often given during a Christian church service

startled (STAR-tuhld) – frightened by being surprised

tomb (TOOM) – a place for holding a dead body

Transylvania (tran-sil-VAIN-yuh) – a real-life mountainous region in eastern Europe

undead (un-DED) – another name for a vampire or zombie

vampire (VAM-pire) – a dead person believed to come out of the grave at night and suck the blood of the living

MORE ABOUT VAMPIRES

Myths and legends of vampires have haunted people for thousands of years. In fact, author Bram Stoker spent seven years researching the many tales about these creepy creatures for his book.

No one knows who told the first vampire stories, but ancient **Mesopotamians** (meh-soh-puh-TAY-mee-ahns) were some of the first. More than 4,000 years ago, these people, from the area of modern-day Iraq, feared an evil goddess called Lamastu. The Mesopotamians believed Lamastu was responsible for many diseases including the death of young children.

Researchers have found tales of blood-sucking creatures all over the world. Most modern legends, however, come from eastern Europe. In fact, many believe the term "vampire" comes from a Russian creature called **Upir** (oo-PEER).

Some myths about vampires are no longer common. For example, eastern Europeans once believed that scattering seeds on the ground could keep vampires away. They thought vampires would stop to count the seeds instead of chasing after their next victim.

Some people believe author Bram Stoker named his character Dracula after a real-life person. In the mid-1400s, Prince Vlad Tepes ruled over what is today Romania. This evil leader was also known as **Vlad Dracula**, meaning "Son of the Dragon."

In the past, some people might have actually returned from the dead! A rare disease called **catalepsy** (KAT-ah-lep-see) can make a person stiff and slow down their breathing. Early doctors sometimes thought these people were dead. When the person eventually woke up, or even escaped from their own grave, they may have been considered a vampire.

Vampire bats are not just found in stories. These winged creatures actually live in parts of Central and South America. They feed on blood from other animals and birds. In fact, vampire bats are the only animals in the world to survive on nothing but blood.

DISCUSSION QUESTIONS

1. In chapter one, Jonathan visits Count Dracula at his castle in Transylvania. Looking back at the story, what clues helped Jonathan realize that the count was a vampire? Do you think he should have figured this out sooner? Why or why not?

2. Do you think the other characters in this story could have stopped Dracula without Dr Van Helsing? Why or why not? List some of the reasons he was important to the story.

3. What were some of Dracula's powers in this story? What were some of his weaknesses? Were these powers and weaknesses different or similar to other vampire stories that you have read? Explain.

WRITING PROMPTS

1. Throughout history, thousands of stories have been written about Dracula and other vampires. Now try to write your own! What will your vampires look like? Who will they haunt? How will your characters stop them?

2. Do you have a favourite scary story? Write it down and share it with your friends and family.

3. In this story, Dracula can turn into a bat and a wolf. If you had the power to turn into any animal, what animal would it be and why? Write about what your adventures as that animal would be like.

OTHER BOOKS

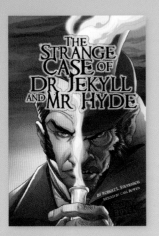

The Strange Case of Dr Jekyll and Mr Hyde

Scientist Dr Henry Jekyll believes every human has two minds: one good and one evil. He develops a potion to separate them from each other. Soon, his evil mind takes over, and Dr Jekyll becomes a hideous fiend known as Mr Hyde.

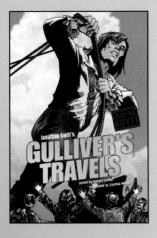

Gulliver's Travels

Lemuel Gulliver always dreamed of sailing across the seas, but he never could have imagined the places his travels would take him. On the island of Lilliput, he is captured by tiny creatures no more than six inches tall. In the country of Blefuscu, he is nearly squashed by an army of giants. His adventures could be the greatest tales ever told, if he survives long enough to tell them.

20,000 Leagues Under the Sea

Scientist Pierre Aronnax and his trusty servant set sail to hunt a sea monster. With help from Ned Land, the world's greatest harpooner, the men soon discover that the creature is really a high-tech submarine. To keep this secret from being revealed, the sub's leader, Captain Nemo, takes the men hostage. Now, each man must decide whether to trust Nemo or try to escape this underwater world.

The War of the Worlds

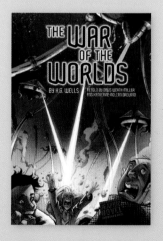

In the late 19th century, a cylinder crashes down near London. When George investigates, a Martian activates an evil machine and begins destroying everything in its path! George must find a way to survive a War of the Worlds.

GRAPHIC REVOLVE

If you have enjoyed this story, there are many more exciting tales for you to discover in the Graphic Revolve collection...

20,000 Leagues Under the Sea

Black Beauty

Dracula

Frankenstein

Gulliver's Travels

The Hound of the Baskervilles

The Hunchback of Notre Dame

King Arthur and the Knights of the Round Table

Robin Hood

The Strange Case of Dr Jekyll and Mr Hyde

Treasure Island

The War of the Worlds